Mary's Lamb

Written by Sarah Josepha Hale

Illustrated by Annie White

HOUGHTON MIFFLIN COMPANY

BOSTON

ATLANTA   DALLAS   GENEVA, ILLINOIS   PALO ALTO   PRINCETON

Mary had a little lamb,

Its fleece was white as snow.

And everywhere that Mary went,

The lamb was sure to go.

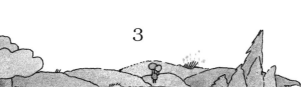

He followed her to school one day —

That was against the rule.

It made the children laugh and play,

To see a lamb at school.

So the teacher turned him out,

But still he lingered near,

And waited patiently about,

Till Mary did appear.

"What makes the lamb love Mary so?"

The eager children cry.

"Oh, Mary loves the lamb, you know,"

The teacher did reply.